Behold...
I Give You Power

SUCCESS PLANNER

DEUTERONOMY 8:18

This planner belongs to:

_____

BEHOLD I GIVE YOU POWER SUCCESS PLANNER.

Please direct all copyright inquiries to: B.O.Y. Enterprises, Inc.
P.O. Box 1012
Lowell, NC 28098

Paperback ISBN: 978-1-7362921-2-9

Cover and Interior Design: B.O.Y. Enterprises, Inc.

Printed in the United States.

Hello there, beautiful!

Welcome to the first day of the rest of your life! You are about to embark on a beautiful new chapter of your life's journey. So are you going to close your eyes and hope for the best, or are you going to walk into your future with purpose and intentionality? This year I'm inviting you to set some intentions for the next twelve months. It's not about perfection, about getting things right, or chasing an invisible idea. Instead, it's about betting on yourself. Every! Single! Day!

Many people ask me why they should bet on themselves and not God. Trust me, I asked God the same question when He told me to bet on myself. Here's the thing though... God has already done His part. He made you in His image and likeness. He sent His son to die for your sins so that you could be restored back to His original intention of dominion and authority over the Earth. Now, it is up to you to trust what God has entrusted to you. Throughout this planner, trust God to reveal His plan to you. As you execute that plan, begin each day with the intention to believe in the investment God has made in you. God is after a return on His investment. He will only get that return when you *bet on yourself*.

Let's get started!

Bet on Yourself

With love,

 **2021** *You were born with everything you need to make this year your best year!*

JANUARY

S	M	T	W	T	F	S
					1	2
3	4	5	6	7	8	9
10	11	12	13	14	15	16
17	18	19	20	21	22	23
24	25	26	27	28	29	30
31						

FEBRUARY

S	M	T	W	T	F	S
	1	2	3	4	5	6
7	8	9	10	11	12	13
14	15	16	17	18	19	20
21	22	23	24	25	26	27
28						

MARCH

S	M	T	W	T	F	S
	1	2	3	4	5	6
7	8	9	10	11	12	13
14	15	16	17	18	19	20
21	22	23	24	25	26	27
28	29	30	31			

APRIL

S	M	T	W	T	F	S
				1	2	3
4	5	6	7	8	9	10
11	12	13	14	15	16	17
18	19	20	21	22	23	24
25	26	27	28	29	30	

MAY

S	M	T	W	T	F	S
						1
2	3	4	5	6	7	8
9	10	11	12	13	14	15
16	17	18	19	20	21	22
23	24	25	26	27	28	29
30	31					

JUNE

S	M	T	W	T	F	S
		1	2	3	4	5
6	7	8	9	10	11	12
13	14	15	16	17	18	19
20	21	22	23	24	25	26
27	28	29	30			

JULY

S	M	T	W	T	F	S
				1	2	3
4	5	6	7	8	9	10
11	12	13	14	15	16	17
18	19	20	21	22	23	24
25	26	27	28	29	30	31

AUGUST

S	M	T	W	T	F	S
1	2	3	4	5	6	7
8	9	10	11	12	13	14
15	16	17	18	19	20	21
22	23	24	25	26	27	28
29	30	31				

SEPTEMBER

S	M	T	W	T	F	S
			1	2	3	4
5	6	7	8	9	10	11
12	13	14	15	16	17	18
19	20	21	22	23	24	25
26	27	28	29	30		

OCTOBER

S	M	T	W	T	F	S
					1	2
3	4	5	6	7	8	9
10	11	12	13	14	15	16
17	18	19	20	21	22	23
24	25	26	27	28	29	30
31						

NOVEMBER

S	M	T	W	T	F	S
	1	2	3	4	5	6
7	8	9	10	11	12	13
14	15	16	17	18	19	20
21	22	23	24	25	26	27
28	29	30				

DECEMBER

S	M	T	W	T	F	S
			1	2	3	4
5	6	7	8	9	10	11
12	13	14	15	16	17	18
19	20	21	22	23	24	25
26	27	28	29	30	31	

IT ALL STARTS WITH YOUR MINDSET
See Yourself Successful

Remember the Lord your God. He is the one who gives you power to be successful, in order to fulfill the covenant he confirmed to your ancestors with an oath. - Deuteronomy 8:18 (NLT)

Every win, manifestation, and success story begins with your mindset. To be successful, one must accept they have been given the POWER to be successful. Yes, most versions of the bible translate this word successful as wealth. We don't want get into a theological debate here, so let's agree to set our minds to accept the power God has given us to become wealthy and successful. You do not have to strive for what has already been given to you. Therefore, we are not "grinding" or "hustling" our way to success. We are trusting God's plans for our lives and partnering with HIM to bring what has been established in Heaven to the earth realm.

A Letter To Myself

Dear _____.

It's time. I am ready to let go of the old, commit to myself and embrace change. I believe that the world is transformed by the choices we make and I know that my life is important. My words, thoughts and actions are powerful.

So I am open to becoming more _____ and choose to do more _____. I am ready to commit to releasing my old stories about who I am and what I am capable of because _____.

God's banner over my life is _____.

I devote myself to spending less time doing things that waste my precious time like _____, _____, & _____ because they make me feel _____, _____, & _____.

The top three things that are important to me are:
1.
2.
3.
...and I am ready to make them a priority in my life. No matter what.

One last thing: I love you and appreciate you _____, because of all of the amazing things you have made it through and all the incredible things you have accomplished. I vow to tell you how amazing you are more often.

Jesus thought you were worth dying for. I think you are worth living for.

With love,

Daydreaming with God

"For I know the plans I have for you," says the Lord. "They are plans for good and not for disaster, to give you a future and a hope. In those days when you pray, I will listen. If you look for me wholeheartedly, you will find me. I will be found by you," says the Lord. "I will end your captivity and restore your fortunes. I will gather you out of the nations where I sent you and will bring you home again to your own land." -Jeremiah 29:11-13 (NLT)

How long has it been since you just sat and daydreamed with God? Some psychologists believe daydreaming keeps your life's agenda in front of you. It is said that daydreaming is a powerful tool used to rehearse new situations, plan for the future, and remind the dreamer of what's in front of them.

When we daydream with God, the one who actually knows the future, we come into agreement with God's plans for our future. We create a visual for our mind to focus on as we navigate the ups and downs of everyday life. Instead of utilizing this planner to write out your plans, use it to write the plans God reveals to you as you daydream with Him.

What are you partnering with God to produce?

"You can make many plans, but the Lord's purpose will prevail" - Proverbs 19:21 (NLT)

Find a quiet space. Take a deep cleansing breath. Turn on your favorite soaking music. Now ask God to reveal His purpose for your life. Ask Him to give you His vision for your future and the steps you need to take to accomplish His goals. Finally, write everything He speaks to you.

_____

_____

_____

_____

_____

_____

_____

_____

_____

_____

_____

_____

_____

_____

_____

_____

_____

_____

_____

_____

Setting Your Goals

DEFINE YOUR INTENTIONS

Even if it doesn't quite feel like it yet, there is a reason why you want what you want. Scripture teaches us in Psalm 37:4-5 that God plants the seed of desire within us when we delight in Him. Then, as we commit to and trust in Him, He brings those desires to pass. Now that you have spent time daydreaming with God, you've received the seed of desire. Next, you must set your intentions to make what you've daydreamed about a reality.

Take a moment to free yourself of the expectations of others. Remember, you're partnering with the ONE who knows the future. Your intentions become your goals. Make sure your intentions are only based on what God has revealed to you... what He has given YOU a desire for!

This is your chance to make those things happen, but first you have to write them down - so you can!

Yearly Goal Setting...

DEFINE YOUR INTENTIONS

This is the place to explore how you want to feel, what you want to do, and whom you want to become in the next year of your life. Write down each of your goals in the following areas of your life.

EMOTIONAL GOALS	PHYSICAL GOALS	CREATIVE GOALS

FINANCIAL GOALS	SPIRITUAL GOALS	RELATIONAL GOALS

Month One

Trust in the Lord with all your heart, and lean not on your own understanding; In all your ways acknowledge Him, and He shall direct your paths.- Proverbs 3:5-6 (NKJV)

Partnering with God...

What comes to mind when you see the phrase, "Partnering with God?" Many Christians are very familiar with the phrase but have no clue how to implement it in their everyday lives. Aside from spending time alone with God daily, how does one become a partner with the ONE who knows and sees all? Rather than give you the answer, I am going to challenge you to be intentional about seeking the Lord this month for ways you can partner with Him and come into agreement with the vision He has for your life and business. Our scripture focus for the month is Proverbs 3:5-6. Again, it is very familiar, but how often do we go about our day making plans and doing what seems to be right, only to later learn we've leaned on our own understanding? When we partner with God we do not leave room for self to take center stage. We consult Him in all things and trust the plan He reveals for our path(S). Yes, there is an "S" on paths! I was shocked when I initially saw it as well!

You've already daydreamed with God about His plans for this year. Now, daydream with Him about His plans for this month!

Monthly Intentions

Date _____

CONFESSION OF FAITH: _____
_____
_____

MONTHLY GOALS

TO DO LIST

- [ ] _____
- [ ] _____
- [ ] _____
- [ ] _____
- [ ] _____
- [ ] _____
- [ ] _____
- [ ] _____
- [ ] _____
- [ ] _____

DATES TO REMEMBER:

January

PARTNERING WITH GOD TO PRODUCE SUCCESS

Trust in the Lord with all your heart. And lean not on your own understanding: In all your ways acknowledge Him. And He shall direct your paths. - **Proverbs 3:5-6 (NKJV)**

SUN	MON	TUE	WED	THU	FRI	SAT
					1	2
3	4	5	6	7	8	9
10	11	12	13	14	15	16
17	18	19	20	21	22	23
24	25	26	27	28	29	30/31

Monthly Review

Take some time to fill out the spaces on the page below to reflect on your goals, any progress that you may have made and the next steps you need to take to make those goals a reality!

Main Goal   Progress Made   Next Steps

Month Two

BOLD FAITH

"I hereby command you: Be strong and courageous; do not be frightened or dismayed, for the Lord your God is with you wherever you go." - Joshua 1:9 (NRSV)

Bold faith for the assignment...

The book of Joshua is quickly becoming one of my favorite books of the Old Testament. I am fascinated by the way God called Joshua into ministry. He essentially said to Joshua, "I know you are an assistant, but it's your turn to be in charge now." (Read the first chapter of Joshua for context.)

Can you imagine if God called you the same way? No years of training, no college degree, no formal ordination service... just a word from God telling you to step up! What if I told you God has called you in this way but a lack of faith in your abilities has caused you to doubt what you know you've heard? In this day and age, we have protocols that have been put in place to prepare leaders, but God's method of calling and equipping His leaders has not changed. He teaches and prepares you long before your number is called. Joshua's training came through his work as an assistant to Moses. When Moses passed away, God did not give Joshua time to grieve. He did not begin a new training program for Joshua. God knew Joshua's former job equipped him for the new assignment.

As you progress through this month, make time to assess how you've been equipped for this new assignment. Yesterday's assignment is over. Today, you embark on a new journey of leadership, purpose, and victory! Don't worry about what you think you don't know. Just as God was preparing Joshua long before Joshua knew he was being prepared, God has been preparing you since birth to walk in your new assignment. Time alone with God will produce details, instructions, and daily guidance to steward what has been given to you. As your task list grows, make sure you always allot time for God to teach you how to win every battle, slay every giant, and walk into your promise!

Use the space below to write any insight you've received for your new assignment.

Monthly Intentions

Date _____

CONFESSION OF FAITH _____

_____

_____

MONTHLY GOALS

TO DO LIST

DATES TO REMEMBER

BOLD FAITH FOR THE ASSIGNMENT

I hereby command you: Be strong and courageous; do not be frightened or dismayed, for the Lord your God is with you wherever you go. **-Joshua 1:9 (NRSV)**

SUN	MON	TUE	WED	THU	FRI	SAT
	1	2	3	4	5	6
7	8	9	10	11	12	13
14	15	16	17	18	19	20
21	22	23	24	25	26	27
28						

Monthly Review

Take some time to fill out the spaces on the page below to reflect on your goals, any progress that you may have made and the next steps you need to take to make those goals a reality!

Main Goal

Progress Made

Next Steps

In your strength I can crush an army; with my God I can scale any wall. God's way is perfect. All the Lord's promises prove true. He is a shield for all who look to him for protection.- 2 Samuel 22:30-31 (NLT)

With God, you are UNSTOPPABLE...

As you enter the third month of your new journey, you may notice the wind trying to leak from your sails. This is the month that has the potential to make or break your success because it is the month many people grow bored and walk away. Others determine the weight of the new assignment is simply too heavy, so they choose to walk away. But not you. Not this time! This time, you are going to keep the vow you made to yourself. This month, you are going to tap into the strength of the Almighty and become unstoppable.

Your foundational scripture for the month reveals what you are capable of when you pull from the strength of God. You can crush any army. You... yes, you... One person fully aligned with God can crush any opponent who dares to try to stop them. You can scale any wall. Any opposition that confronts you becomes another opportunity for you to beat the odds. It is a chance for God to show up and empower you with the ideas and strategies that produce the desired outcome. You'll no longer stare at the brick wall! This time, you will climb right over it.

This is the month you press your way to the promises of God! Instead of buckling under pressure, gird yourself in truth and keep going! Your victory has been guaranteed! With the strength of the Lord at your disposal, you are UNSTOPPABLE!

Use the space below to write scriptures that help you remember God is with you.

Monthly Intentions

MONTHLY GOALS

TO DO LIST

March

WITH GOD, YOU ARE UNSTOPPABLE

In your strength I can crush an army: with my God I can scale any wall. God's way is perfect. All the Lord's promises prove true. He is a shield for all who look to him for protection. **2 Samuel 22:30-31 (NLT)**

SUN	MON	TUE	WED	THU	FRI	SAT
	1	2	3	4	5	6
7	8	9	10	11	12	13
14	15	16	17	18	19	20
21	22	23	24	25	26	27
28	29	30	31			

Monthly Review

Take some time to fill out the spaces on the page below to reflect on your goals, any progress that you may have made and the next steps you need to take to make those goals a reality!

Main Goal   *Progress Made*   *Next Steps*

WELCOME TO THE 2ND QUARTER

Month Four

- A NEW THING -

Do not remember the former things, or ponder the things of the past. "Listen carefully, I am about to do a new thing, Now it will spring forth; Will you not be aware of it? I will even put a road in the wilderness, rivers in the desert." -Isaiah 43:18-19 (AMP)

Are you ready for the NEW thing?

Welcome to the 2nd Quarter! This month is vital, not just because it's the beginning of a new quarter, but also because it is a new opportunity for you to partner with God to produce something new in your life and business. Your foundational scripture for the month is an excellent reminder of what happens when you believe God for a NEW thing.

The first quarter of the year may not have gone the way you envisioned it, and that's okay. Isaiah 43:18 encourages us to forget the former things. Realign your thought process so that yesterday's let-down does not hinder the promotion of today. On the other hand, you may have had a fantastic first quarter. In that case, you still can't settle for yesterday's success. God has a NEW thing prepared for you!

We all know there are no rivers in deserts or roads in the wilderness, but God is saying He has a miracle prepared for you. Your responsibility is to have the faith to pull your NEW thing out of Heaven. It is your job to tune your ear o the frequency of Heaven and believe God for what He reveals to you as you spend time alone with Him.

Spend the next few minutes communicating with God and listening to what He has to say about your today. Use the space below to write what He reveals.

Monthly Intentions

Date _____

CONFESSION OF FAITH: _____

_____

_____

MONTHLY GOALS

- ⬡
- ⬡
- ⬡
- ⬡

DATES TO REMEMBER:

TO DO LIST

☐ _____

☐ _____

☐ _____

☐ _____

☐ _____

☐ _____

☐ _____

☐ _____

☐ _____

☐ _____

April

A NEW THING

Do not remember the former things. or ponder the things of the past. "Listen carefully. I am about to do a new thing. Now it will spring forth: Will you not be aware of it? I will even put a road in the wilderness. rivers in the desert." **-Isaiah 43:18-19 (AMP)**

SUN	MON	TUE	WED	THU	FRI	SAT
				1	2	3
4	5	6	7	8	9	10
11	12	13	14	15	16	17
18	19	20	21	22	23	24
25	26	27	28	29	30	

Monthly Review

Take some time to fill out the spaces on the page below to reflect on your goals, any progress that you may have made and the next steps you need to take to make those goals a reality!

Main Goal   Progress Made   Next Steps

Month Five

Each time he said, "My grace is all you need. My power works best in weakness. -2 Corinthians 12:9 (NLT)

You have been graced for this race

Welcome to the 2nd Quarter! This month is vital, not just because it's the beginning of a new quarter, but also because it is a new opportunity for you to partner with God to produce something new in your life and business. Your foundational scripture for the month is an excellent reminder of what happens when you believe God for a NEW thing.

The first quarter of the year may not have gone the way you envisioned it, and that's okay. Isaiah 43:18 encourages us to forget the former things. Realign your thought process so that yesterday's let-down does not hinder the promotion of today. On the other hand, you may have had a fantastic first quarter. In that case, you still can't settle for yesterday's success. God has a NEW thing prepared for you!

We all know there are no rivers in deserts or roads in the wilderness, but God is saying He has a miracle prepared for you. Your responsibility is to have the faith to pull your NEW thing out of Heaven. It is your job to tune your ear o the frequency of Heaven and believe God for what He reveals to you as you spend time alone with Him.

Spend the next few minutes communicating with God and listening to what He has to say about your today. Use the space below to write what He reveals.

_____

_____

_____

_____

_____

_____

_____

Monthly Intentions

Date _____

CONFESSION OF FAITH: _____

_____

_____

MONTHLY GOALS

⬡ _____

⬡ _____

⬡ _____

⬡ _____

⬡ _____

DATES TO REMEMBER:

TO DO LIST

☐ _____

☐ _____

☐ _____

☐ _____

☐ _____

☐ _____

☐ _____

☐ _____

☐ _____

☐ _____

May

GRACED FOR THIS RACE

"Each time he said, "My grace is all you need. My power works best in weakness." -2 Corinthians 12:9 (NLT)

SUN	MON	TUE	WED	THU	FRI	SAT
1/2	3	4	5	6	7	8
9	10	11	12	13	14	15
16	17	18	19	20	21	22
23	24	25	26	27	28	29
30	31					

Monthly Review

Take some time to fill out the spaces on the page below to reflect on your goals, any progress that you may have made and the next steps you need to take to make those goals a reality!

Main Goal   *Progress Made*   *Next Steps*

Month Six

- CENTER STAGE -

A man's gift [given in love or courtesy] makes room for him and brings him before great men.
-Proverbs 18:16 AMP

Prepare to take Center Stage...

Many Christians wrongfully believe they are intended to live in the background. They somehow equate hiding their talents with humility. It is often difficult to break this belief, but when God highlights you, there is no place on Earth for you to hide.

God has traveled with you on a transformational journey this year. This journey wasn't intended to be hidden. You have been given a gift so that you may be given as a gift to those who desperately need you. As this month's foundational scripture suggests, the gift inside of you makes room for you. That means no matter how crowded your industry may seem, your gift is literally creating space for you on the stage. It is creating a pathway for "great men" in your industry to see you, acknowledge you, and make room for you to stand next to them on the center stage.

This is your moment to embrace the spotlight. The more people who know you, the more people you can introduce to the love of God. This spotlight is not for your personal gain. It is to be used for the glory of God so that people from all over the world may know of Him by your great gift!

In the space below, list 5 ways you can prepare for the center stage this month.

_____

_____

_____

_____

_____

_____

_____

Monthly Intentions

Date _____

CONFESSION OF FAITH: _____
_____
_____

MONTHLY GOALS

⬡
⬡
⬡
⬡
⬡

DATES TO REMEMBER:

TO DO LIST

☐ _____
☐ _____
☐ _____
☐ _____
☐ _____
☐ _____
☐ _____
☐ _____
☐ _____
☐ _____

June

CENTER STAGE

"A man's gift [given in love or courtesy] makes room for him and brings him before great men.
-Proverbs 18:16 (AMP)

SUN	MON	TUE	WED	THU	FRI	SAT
		1	2	3	4	5
6	7	8	9	10	11	12
13	14	15	16	17	18	19
20	21	22	23	24	25	26
27	28	29	30			

Monthly Review

Take some time to fill out the spaces on the page below to reflect on your goals, any progress that you may have made and the next steps you need to take to make those goals a reality!

Main Goal   *Progress Made*   *Next Steps*

Month Seven

And by the seventh day God completed His work which He had done, and He rested (ceased) on the seventh day from all His work which He had done. So God blessed the seventh day and sanctified it [as His own, that is, set it apart as holy from other days], because in it He rested from all His work which He had created and done. -Genesis 2:2-3 AMP

Rest is divine...

There is a popular saying in the entrepreneurship sphere that states, "the grind never sleeps". Each time I see this quote, I cringed because it makes me envision bloodshot eyes, coupled with gallon-sized bags caused by sleep deprivation. I imagine a person nodding off in front of their computer as they attempt to complete "one more task" before bed. While I intimately understand the need to meet deadlines, I also understand the damage caused by pushing one's self beyond healthy limits.

As a Kingdom Entrepreneur, we are called to follow biblical principles as we execute our tasks in business. Our monthly foundational scripture is a great reminder of the importance of including rest as an intentional part of the creation cycle. God, the ultimate creator, created for 6 days, then rested on the seventh. Utilizing His system gives us an opportunity to examine what we've created, then take time to appreciate the fruits of our labor.

For many people, rest comes in the form of vacations. For others, it comes from taking days off, reading for enjoyment, long bubble baths, or simply spending time with loved ones. Your choice OF rest is up to you. The choice TO rest is not! If we are going to follow biblical principles, we must follow them all.

Use the space below to plan your intentional rest this month.

Monthly Intentions

Date

MONTHLY GOALS

TO DO LIST

July

DIVINE REST

And by the seventh day God completed His work which He had done, and He rested (ceased) on the seventh day from all His work which He had done. So God blessed the seventh day and sanctified it [as His own, that is, set it apart as holy from other days], because in it He rested from all His work which He had created and done.

-Genesis 2:2-3 (AMP)

SUN	MON	TUE	WED	THU	FRI	SAT
			1	2	3	
4	5	6	7	8	9	10
11	12	13	14	15	16	17
18	19	20	21	22	23	24
25	26	27	28	29	30	31

Monthly Review

The intention behind this month, what I hoped to accomplish, and the broader goals I was working toward as I reflect on the progress and consider the path ahead.

Main Goal   Progress Made   Next Steps

Month Eight

- RETURN ON INVESTMENT -

Then Isaac planted [seed] in that land [as a farmer] and reaped in the same year a hundred times [as much as he had planted], and the Lord blessed and favored him. -Genesis 26:12 AMP

Kingdom investments yield positive returns

There was once a farmer who wandered about looking for the land God desired for him to dwell in. He had a generational promise, but he wasn't seeing the manifestation of that promise. In obedience to God, that farmer planted a seed in an unfamiliar land. Not long after, that seed produced a great harvest for the farmer and he became far wealthier than all of the other farmers in the land. That farmer was Isaac, who is mentioned in our foundational scripture. His life was changed as a result of a single seed which produced a great harvest for him. Think of all the seeds you've sown this year. Have you seen the type of return you expected?

Just as you expect a return when you invest in the stock market, you should also expect a return when you invest in the Kingdom. As you are following God's instructions for your life and business, you should anticipate seeing a positive return in the form of God's manifested promises. Many times Christians do not see a return on their investments because they do not have an expectation of a return. They say things like, "I'm not looking for anything in return. I just want to be obedient to God." While this thought process may sound noble, it lacks faith for there is no hope of a return.

God desires for His sons and daughters to recognize Him as a keeper of His promises. He wants us to know He pays much larger returns than the stock market ever will. Use the space below to write down the Kingdom investments you've made this year, and the returns you'd like to see this month.

.

Monthly Intentions

Date _____

CONFESSION OF FAITH: _____

_____

_____

MONTHLY GOALS

-
-
-
-

DATES TO REMEMBER:

TO DO LIST

- [ ] _____
- [ ] _____
- [ ] _____
- [ ] _____
- [ ] _____
- [ ] _____
- [ ] _____
- [ ] _____
- [ ] _____
- [ ] _____

August

RETURN ON INVESTMENT

*"Then Isaac planted [seed] in that land [as a farmer] and reaped in the same year a hundred times [as much as he had planted], and the Lord blessed and favored him." -**Genesis 26:12 (AMP)***

SUN	MON	TUE	WED	THU	FRI	SAT
1	2	3	4	5	6	7
8	9	10	11	12	13	14
15	16	17	18	19	20	21
22	23	24	25	26	27	28
29	30	31				

Monthly Review

Take some time to fill out the spaces on the page below to reflect on your goals, any progress that you may have made and the next steps you need to take to make those goals a reality.

| Main Goal | Progress Made | Next Steps |

Month Nine

- GIVING BIRTH TO PROMISE -

Not a single one of all the good promises the Lord had given to the family of Israel was left unfulfilled; everything he had spoken came true. -Joshua 21:45 NLT

Promise is birthed from proper positioning

If you read the book of Joshua, you will see that from beginning to end Joshua was put in positions that required him to fight. After the death of Moses, God chose Joshua to lead the children of Israel into what seemed to be an impossible battle to win. Yet, Joshua believed that as long as the Lord was with them, they would always be victorious. He was right!

The greatest opposition to your victory is your belief system. If you see your situation as insurmountable, you will set yourself up to lose before the battle ever begins. If you position yourself as God's chosen vessel to lead His people into victory, you will win. That is God's promise to you... that He will always cause you to triumph. (2 Corinthians 2:14).

In order for a mother to give birth naturally, she must be in the birthing position. Our foundational scripture this month reminds us how God fulfilled every promise He made to the children of Israel. It took years for those promises to be birthed because the children of Israel were not in the proper position to give birth. They were murmuring and complaining when they should have been in a posture of trust and gratitude.

Take a moment to review your own life and business. Has an improper posture stopped you from giving birth to the promise? If so, this is your month to correct your posture and pull on Heaven for the manifestation of the promises of God. You've won the battles, now it's time to SEE the promises with your natural eyes! Use the space below to write the promises you're positioning yourself to receive.

_____

_____

_____

_____

_____

_____

Monthly Intentions

Date _____

CONFESSION OF FAITH: _____

_____

_____

MONTHLY GOALS

- ⬡
- ⬡
- ⬡
- ⬡

DATES TO REMEMBER:

TO DO LIST

- ☐ _____
- ☐ _____
- ☐ _____
- ☐ _____
- ☐ _____
- ☐ _____
- ☐ _____
- ☐ _____
- ☐ _____

September

GIVING BIRTH TO PROMISE

Not a single one of all the good promises the Lord had given to the family of Israel was left unfulfilled; everything he had spoken came true. **-Joshua 21:45 (NLT)**

SUN	MON	TUE	WED	THU	FRI	SAT
			1	2	3	4
5	6	7	8	9	10	11
12	13	14	15	16	17	18
19	20	21	22	23	24	25
26	27	28	29	30		

Monthly Review

Take some time to fill out the spaces on the page below to reflect on your goals, any progress that you may have made and the next steps you need to take to make those goals a reality!

Main Goal   Progress Made   Next Steps

Month Ten

Don't be misled - you cannot mock the justice of God. You will always harvest what you plant.
-Galatians 6:7 NLT

Harvest is your responsibility

Our foundational scripture this month is a gentle reminder of the partnership you have with God. On the surface, this scripture seems like a warning to watch your behavior because you will reap what you sow. While this is true, this scripture goes much deeper. It is a God-guarantee that the seeds you've sown will yield a harvest. You've spent the year sowing seeds for your business. You've sown seeds of faith, consistency, obedience, and finances. These seeds have been sown into the fields of Heaven and have produced a harvest for you. However, the harvesting of your crops is your responsibility. Natural crops will not jump out of the field into the farmer's barn. No, the farmer must go into the field to collect the fruit of his labor. Likewise, the reaping of your harvest will require you to work.

The scripture states YOU will always harvest what YOU plant. This month as you set your intentions, begin to seek the Lord for how you can harvest what you have planted. For some, you may release your harvesting angels to collect your harvest and bring it to you. For others, you may need to pick up the phone and begin making calls to those who are in a position to help you advance in your industry. Others may need to do both of these things. Only God knows exactly what your harvesting process will look like.

Spend the next few minutes communicating with God about your harvesting process and use the space below to write the instructions He gives you.

_____

_____

_____

_____

_____

_____

_____

Monthly Intentions

Date _____

CONFESSION OF FAITH: _____

_____

_____

MONTHLY GOALS

- ⬡
- ⬡
- ⬡
- ⬡
- ⬡

DATES TO REMEMBER:

TO DO LIST

- ☐ _____
- ☐ _____
- ☐ _____
- ☐ _____
- ☐ _____
- ☐ _____
- ☐ _____
- ☐ _____
- ☐ _____
- ☐ _____

October

YOUR HARVEST IS GUARANTEED

SUN	MON	TUE	WED	THU	FRI	SAT
					1	2
3	4	5	6	7	8	9
10	11	12	13	14	15	16
17	18	19	20	21	22	23
24	25	26	27	28	29	30

Monthly Review

Take some time to fill out the spaces on the page below to reflect on your goals, any progress that you may have made and the next steps you need to take to make those goals a reality!

Main Goal

Progress Made

Next Steps

Month Eleven

GRATITUDE IS GOLDEN

Yes, you will be enriched in every way so that you can always be generous. And when we take your gifts to those who need them, they will thank God. So two good things will result from this ministry of giving—the needs of the believers in Jerusalem will be met, and they will joyfully express their thanks to God.
-2 Corinthians 9:11-12 NLT

Gratitude is currency...

As a successful Kingdom Entrepreneur, it can be easy to slip into the belief that you always have to have money to accomplish things. However, our foundational scripture this month gives us an example of how gratitude can be given in exchange for goods. No, I am not saying you can go into a store and pay with a "thank you". Yet, you can receive a mighty blessing from God which has the power to completely change your situation and the only thing He'll expect from you is gratitude.

Sometimes we forget that God's ways are not our ways and the ways of Heaven are not always the ways of the Earth. From an Earthly perspective, you may be expected to repay the person who gives you groceries when your family is experiencing financial hardships. From a Heavenly perspective, you are expected to give thanks to God for His goodness and the favor He bestowed upon the person who blessed you.

During this month, when more people are helping the less fortunate and considering the things they are grateful for, consider your list of things you owe God gratitude for. Your gratitude is all the payment God requires. God has blessed us beyond measure this year, the very least we can do is repay His generosity with our words of thanks and praise.

Use the space below to write your words of gratitude. As you set your intentions this month, remember to be intentional about spending your currency of gratitude.

_____

_____

_____

_____

_____

_____

_____

Monthly Intentions

Date _____

CONFESSION OF FAITH: _____
_____
_____

MONTHLY GOALS

- ⬢
- ⬢
- ⬢
- ⬢
- ⬢

DATES TO REMEMBER:

TO DO LIST

- [ ] _____
- [ ] _____
- [ ] _____
- [ ] _____
- [ ] _____
- [ ] _____
- [ ] _____
- [ ] _____
- [ ] _____
- [ ] _____

November

GRATITUDE IS CURRENCY

Yes, you will be enriched in every way so that you can always be generous. And when we take your gifts to those who need them, they will thank God. So two good things will result from this ministry of giving—the needs of the believers in Jerusalem will be met, and they will joyfully express their thanks to God. **-2 Corinthians 9:11-12 (NLT)**

SUN	MON	TUE	WED	THU	FRI	SAT
	1	2	3	4	5	6
7	8	9	10	11	12	13
14	15	16	17	18	19	20
21	22	23	24	25	26	27
28	29	30				

Monthly Review

Take some time to fill out the spaces on the page below to reflect on your goals, any progress that you may have made and the next steps you need to take to make those goals a reality!

Main Goal   *Progress Made*   *Next Steps*

Month Twelve

-IN HIS PLAN-

For I know the plans I have for you," says the Lord. "They are plans for good and not for disaster, to give you a future and a hope. -Jeremiah 29:11 NLT

All in His plan...

Welcome to the last month of the year. You have been intentional about your life and business all year long. That alone is worthy of celebration. It is important to remember whether or not you reached every goal you set for yourself, you are still successful because you remained in alignment with God all year!

Let's take a moment to celebrate THAT!!! (Seriously... pat yourself on the back right now.)

Now, as you review the year, consider where you need to make adjustments in the future so that you can see even more success. Ask yourself if the things you did not achieve were your plans or God's plans. God's plans are always linked to hope. They end with a positive outcome for you, even when it doesn't feel like it.

Use the space below to allow God to reveal more of His plans for you. This is the end of a calendar year, but it is not the end of God's plans toward you! He has a future for you! He has victory for you! He has joy and hope for you! Continue partnering with God to bring His plans to pass in your life! Remember, God is not a man that He should lie, nor is He the son of man that He should repent. If God said it, that settles it!

Monthly Intentions

Date _____

CONFESSION OF FAITH: _____
_____
_____

MONTHLY GOALS

⬡
⬡
⬡

DATES TO REMEMBER:

TO DO LIST

IN HIS PLAN

SUN	MON	TUE	WED	THU	FRI	SAT
			1	2	3	4
5	6	7	8	9	10	11
12	13	14	15	16	17	18
19	20	21	22	23	24	25
26	27	28	29	30	31	

Monthly Review

Take some time to fill out the spaces on the page below to reflect on your goals, any progress that you may have made and the next steps you need to take to make those goals a reality!

Main Goal	Progress Made	Next Steps

Let's review your yearly goals...

HOW DID YOU DO?

Go back to the goals you wrote at the beginning of the year. Did you achieve all of those goals? If not, take some time to examine what stopped you from reaching the goals you missed. What do you need to do differently next year to be more successful?

EMOTIONAL GOALS	PHYSICAL GOALS	CREATIVE GOALS

FINANCIAL GOALS	SPIRITUAL GOALS	RELATIONAL GOALS

About the Author

Otescia Johnson is a captivating Speaker, Writer, and Minister. She is the founder of B.O.Y. Enterprises, Inc. and the bestselling author of 12 published books. Her courses, programs, books, talks, and services are all purposed to help entrepreneurs merge the gap between their faith and the business world.

In addition to writing both books and films, Otescia is an innovative speaker that seeks to shift the mindset of the willing from complacency and stunted growth to living as a magnet for all things intended for their lives.

Visit my website
www.otesciajohnson.com

Follow me on Instagram
@O.R.Johnson

Follow me on Facebook
@AuthorORJohnson

"Remember the only hindrance to your goals is what lies in your mind."

-Otescia Johnson